THE ADVENT SEQUENCE
VENI EMMANUEL

GW00584810

ıN ADVENT CAROL SERVICE
AND ADVENT RESOURCES
COMPILED BY
DAVID OGDEN & PETER MOGER

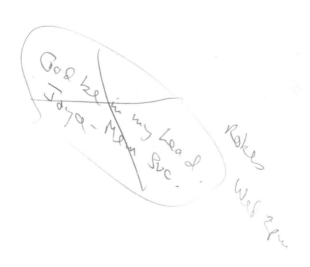

RS✦M

RS☀M

The Royal School of Church Music
19 The Close, Salisbury, Wiltshire, SP1 2EB, England
Tel: +44 (0)1722 424848 Fax: +44 (0)1722 424849
Email: press@rscm.com Website: www.rscm.com
Registered charity 312828

The Advent Sequence
Veni Emmanuel

Texts of the introduction, commentaries, music and graphic images are
copyright © 2009 The Royal School of Church Music,
except where otherwise attributed.

The prayers and service, from *Common Worship: Times and Seasons,* are
copyright © 2006 The Archbishops' Council, and used with permission.

Bible readings are copyright © 1989, 1995 New Revised Standard Version Bible: Anglicized Edition,
Division of Christian Education of the National Council of the Churches of Christ
in the United States of America.
Used by permission. All rights reserved.

First published June 2009

RSCM Order Code: S0127
RSCM Catalogue Number: RS38
ISBN: 978-0-85402-170-3

Cover design by Zednik Productions
Cover picture: The Tree of Jesse, from 'De Laudibus Sancte Crucis'
by Rabanaus Maurus (c.780–856) from Anchin Abbey (vellum)
Music and text origination by RSCM Press and MusicLines
Printed in Great Britain by Caligraving Ltd

Contents

INTRODUCTION

In the Middle Ages, the Church kept Advent as a season of great solemnity – a time in which to meditate upon the ultimate issues of death, judgement, hell and heaven. Advent, though, was also a time of great rejoicing. For Christ would come, not only as Judge, but also as Saviour, and would usher in the Kingdom of God. Advent, therefore, provided a vivid preparation for Christmas. Processions from west to east, and the use of lights, spoke of the Church's hope in the coming of Christ – the Light of the world – to banish sin and darkness. Antiphons were sung, calling upon God to deliver his people, and readings from the Old Testament were seen as pointing to the fulfilment of God's purposes in Jesus.

This service aims to recapture something of that Advent longing and hope. It begins in darkness with the Advent Responsory, in which Christ's coming is announced 'from afar'. The Blessing of Light follows, and, as the service unfolds, the Light is carried to other parts of the church as the procession moves from west to east. The central core of the service is structured around the great Advent Antiphons, known as the Great 'Os'. These were sung originally as Antiphons to the Magnificat at the Evening Office from 17th to 23rd December, and have provided a rich source of devotional imagery in Advent. The readings and music complement the Antiphons, and help us reflect on the theme of the Christ who comes to judge and save his people. The Antiphons are gathered together in the final hymn, O come, O come, Emmanuel, which is sung as the procession withdraws. The service ends in quietness, but in confident hope in the One who is to come. Even so come, Lord Jesus.

STAGING THE SERVICE

Processional movement

The service is built around movement from West to East. In some buildings it might be possible to move everyone (ministers, singers and congregation) at various points throughout the service. In other places, the potential for movement might be more limited, and only ministers and singers may be able to move. The service envisages up to 6 locations throughout the service, with movement between them:

1. The West end (Gathering)
2. The head of the Nave (around a Nave altar or at the Chancel step)
3. The Chancel
4. The East end (at the High altar)
5. The Chancel
6. The West end (Dismissal)

If the limitations of the building mean that it is not possible to use all these locations, then there should at least be movement from West to East (and back again), using 1, 3 and 6.

Darkness & light, sound & silence

The service plays on the strong visual contrast between darkness and light. The service should begin in darkness - or as near to darkness as possible. (It is suggested that main lighting of the church be switched off about 5 minutes before the start of the service). The lighting of the Advent Candle and Blessing of the Light (page 2) should be followed by the sharing of light among the congregation during the Processional Hymn (page 4). For this, each member of the congregation will need a small candle, with a drip shield. The sharing of light is greatly helped by assistants with tapers to pass the light to those at the end of each row of seating. The Advent Candle should always lead any processional movement, representing the light of Christ who goes before his people.

The service begins and ends quietly. It is recommended that, before the service begins, the ministers and singers should move in silence to the West end and that 30–45 seconds of silence should be kept before the opening Responsory (page 1) is sung. Similarly, at the end, a similar silence should be kept between the final Dismissal and any post-service organ music.

Antiphon, Scripture and reflection

For each of the Antiphons, the service offers a related passage of Scripture and musical reflection (through choral items and congregational hymns and songs). It is important that the flow of antiphons, readings and music is gentle and unhurried, and that sufficient silence is allowed, particularly after each of the readings. The Prayers, likewise need to be allowed sufficient space. As well as silent and spoken prayer, they include a hymn or song, which should be sung reflectively, the congregation maintaining the same posture as for the prayers.

The Music

Advent has a rich repertoire of anthems and hymns but sometimes it is hard to find pieces that express the exact mood of the season. It is hoped that this sequence will provide a chance to reflect on the relative simplicity and anticipatory nature of Advent as an antidote to the busyness of the run up to Christmas.

You do not have to sing everything. Try to make the service flow and create variety by adding dynamics to the hymns and assigning verses to different groups: soloists; a small group; the choir and congregation. The addition of instruments will give an added dimension although these should not dominate. Like the RSCM's other service *The Way of the Cross*, the service needs 'space' with time for reflection after the readings. Look for ways to make the service as unhurried as possible, maybe having the readings read by a member of the congregation sitting in their place.

Advent is also a joyful time so the pieces should be sung with commitment and vitality. We hope that this sequence will allow churches to truly reflect the wonder and mystery of the season.

More performing notes, instrumental parts and a template for a congregational service booklet are available to download from the RSCM website:
www.rscm.com/adventsequence

OUTLINE OF THE SERVICE

The Gathering

I – O Sapiens

II – O Adonaï

III – O Radix Jesse

IV – O Clavis David

V – O Oriens

VI – O Rex Gentium

VII – O Emmanuel

The Conclusion

THE ADVENT SEQUENCE

PART I: THE SERVICE

¶ THE GATHERING

The ministers and singers (may) move to the West End

Advent Responsory

Words: First Responsory of Advent Sunday (Office of Matins)

Music: Trevor Jarvis (b.1946)

TO NEXT PAGE 3

The blessing of the light

CANTOR   CHOIR

You, O Lord, are my lamp: **you turn our dark-ness in - to light.**

CANTOR   CHOIR

With you, O Lord, is the well__ of life: **in your light shall we see light.**

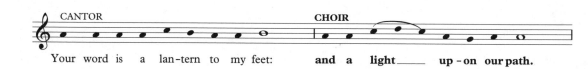

CANTOR   CHOIR

Your word is a lan-tern to my feet: **and a light_____ up - on our path.**

The Advent Candle is lit

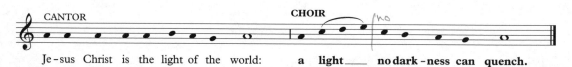

CANTOR   CHOIR

Je-sus Christ is the light of the world: **a light_____ no dark-ness can quench.**

a choral version of these versicles and responses can be found on page 50

PETER COX.

PRESIDENT or CANTOR

Bles - sed are you, Lord our God, King of the universe, eternal creator of day and night.

Now, as darkness is falling, hear the prayer of your faith - ful peo - ple.

Wash a - way our transgressions, cleanse us by your re-fin - ing fire,

and make us tem-ples of your Ho - ly Spi - rit. May we live in watchfulness

as we wait for the coming of your Son Je-sus Christ, who shall judge the world and all its works.

Rouse us from the sleep of sin and make us ready to en - ter your King - dom

where songs of praise for ev - er sound. For you are the true light, who lightens everyone,

and the new heavens and the new earth join to sing your praise

ALL

now and for ev - er - more. A - - men.

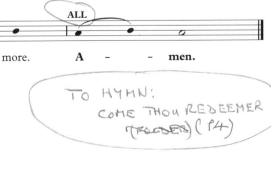

TO HYMN:
COME THOU REDEEMER
(FOLDER) (P4)

Processional Hymn: Come, thou Redeemer of the earth

during which the light, from which the congregation's candles are now lit,
moves in procession to the Nave Altar
(or equivalent place – i.e. not to the East End of the church)

PUER NOBIS NASCITUR

Music: M Praetorius (1571–1621)
arranged by G R Woodward (1848–1934)

A –   –   men.

The choir alone may sing verse 1

1 Come, thou Redeemer of the earth,   AT WEST END
And manifest thy virgin-birth:
Let every age adoring fall,
Such birth befits the God of all.

2 Begotten of no human will,
But of the Spirit, thou art still
The Word of God, in flesh arrayed,
The Saviour, now to man displayed.

3 The virgin womb that burden gained
With virgin honour all unstained,
The banners there of virtue glow,
God in his temple dwells below.

MEN
UNISON

4 From God the Father he proceeds,
To God the Father back he speeds,
Runs out his course to death and hell,
Returns on God's high throne to dwell.

5 O equal to thy Father, thou!
HARMONY Gird on thy fleshly mantle now,
The weakness of our mortal state
With deathless might invigorate.

6 O Jesu, Virgin-born, to thee
Eternal praise and glory be,
Whom with the Father we adore
And Holy Spirit, evermore. Amen. H

Veni, Redemptor gentium, Ambrose of Milan (340–397)
translated by John M Neale (1818–1866)

¶ O SAPIENTIA

Chant: Veni, redemptor gentium
arranged by David Ogden (b.1966)
and Peter Moger (b.1964)

O___ Wis - dom, com-ing forth from the mouth of the___ most high,__
rea- ching from one end to the o - ther migh - ti - ly,__
and sweet - ly or - der - ing all___ things:
Come and teach___ us the way___ of___ pru - dence.

Reading

Wisdom praises herself, and tells of her glory in the midst of her people. In the assembly of the Most High she opens her mouth, and in the presence of his hosts she tells of her glory:

'I came forth from the mouth of the Most High, and covered the earth like a mist. I dwelt in the highest heavens, and my throne was in a pillar of cloud. Alone I compassed the vault of heaven and traversed the depths of the abyss. Over waves of the sea, over all the earth, and over every people and nation I have held sway. Among all these I sought a resting-place; in whose territory should I abide? 'Then the Creator of all things gave me a command, and my Creator chose the place for my tent. He said, "Make your dwelling in Jacob, and in Israel receive your inheritance." Before the ages, in the beginning, he created me, and for all the ages I shall not cease to be.

Ecclesiasticus 24: 1–9

Silence is kept

Anthem/Carol

John Barnard: This is the truth sent from above (page 52)
or
Peter Moger: Where shall wisdom be found? (page 57)
or
Margaret Rizza: Lord, all truth is from you (page 62)

¶ O ADONAÏ

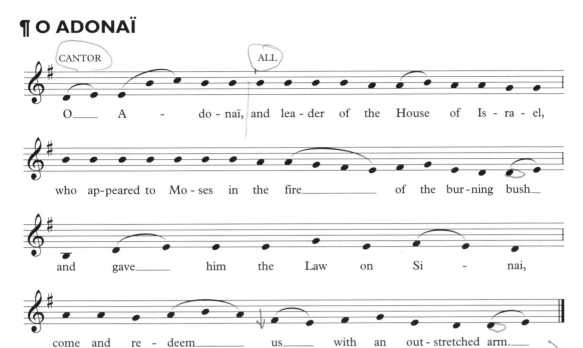

O__ A - do - naï, and lea - der of the House of Is - ra - el,

who ap-peared to Mo - ses in the fire_____ of the bur - ning bush__

and gave_____ him the Law on Si - nai,

come and re - deem_____ us____ with an out - stretched arm.___

Reading

Moses was keeping the flock of his father-in-law Jethro, the priest of Midian; he led his flock beyond the wilderness, and came to Horeb, the mountain of God. There the angel of the Lord appeared to him in a flame of fire out of a bush; he looked, and the bush was blazing, yet it was not consumed.

Then Moses said, 'I must turn aside and look at this great sight, and see why the bush is not burned up.' When the Lord saw that he had turned aside to see, God called to him out of the bush, 'Moses, Moses!' And he said, 'Here I am.'

Then he said, 'Come no closer! Remove the sandals from your feet, for the place on which you are standing is holy ground.' He said further, 'I am the God of your father, the God of Abraham, the God of Isaac, and the God of Jacob.' And Moses hid his face, for he was afraid to look at God.

Exodus 3: 1–6

Silence is kept

Hymn: My God, how wonderful thou art

during which the light moves in procession to the Chancel (i.e. further east)

WESTMINSTER

Music: James Turle (1802–1882)
descant: David Ogden (b.1966)

Last verse descant

7. Fa - ther _ of Je - sus, love's _ re-ward, what rap - ture _ will it be, _____

pro - strate be-fore thy _ throne to lie, and gaze and gaze _ on thee. _____

U 1   My God, how wonderful thou art,
         thy majesty how bright,
         how beautiful thy mercy-seat,
         in depths of burning light!

H 2   How dread are thine eternal years,
         O everlasting Lord,
         by angel spirits day and night
         incessantly adored!

MEN 3 How wonderful, how beautiful,
         the sight of thee must be,
         thine endless wisdom, boundless power,
         and aweful purity!

4*   O how I fear thee, living God,
         with deepest, tenderest fears,
         and worship thee with trembling hope,
         and penitential tears!

LADIES 5* Yet I may love thee too, O Lord,
         almighty as thou art,
         for thou hast stooped to ask of me
         the love of my poor heart.

H 6   No earthly father loves like thee,
         no mother, e'er so mild,
         bears and forbears as thou hast done
         with me thy sinful child.

last verse descant opposite

U 7   Father of Jesus, love's reward,
         what rapture will it be,
         prostrate before thy throne to lie,
         and gaze and gaze on thee!

To PAGE 12

Frederick William Faber (1814–1863)

alternative hymn

Hymn: Lord, I come, longing to know you

Words and music: Geraldine Latty (b.1963)

1. Lord, I come, — long-ing to know you, Lord, I come, drawn by — your

love; Lord, I come, — long-ing to see — your face, — for you

called me to come in-to the ho-li-est — place. — 1. Lord, I come

1, 4 (4th time *Fine*)

1st time to verse 1
2nd time to verse 2 and Fine
D.%

2. Lord, I come, because of Jesus,
   Lord, I come, because he came;
   Lord, I bow, as you reveal your face,
   you have called me to come into the holiest place.

¶ O RADIX JESSE

O___ Root___ of Jes-se, stand-ing as a sign a-mong_ the peo-ples;
be-fore you kings___ will shut___ their___ mouths,_
to you___ the na-tions will make their prayer:
Come and de-li-ver us___ and de-lay no lon-ger.

Reading

A shoot shall come out from the stock of Jesse, and a branch shall grow out
of his roots. The spirit of the Lord shall rest on him, the spirit of wisdom
and understanding, the spirit of counsel and might, the spirit of knowledge
and the fear of the Lord. His delight shall be in the fear of the Lord. He shall
not judge by what his eyes see, or decide by what his ears hear; but with
righteousness he shall judge the poor, and decide with equity for the meek of
the earth.

On that day the root of Jesse shall stand as a signal to the peoples; the nations
shall inquire of him, and his dwelling shall be glorious.

Isaiah 11: 1–4a, 10

Silence is kept

TO PAGE 70

Anthem/Carol

Jon Banks: Of a rose, a lovely rose (page 64)
or
Simon Lole: A tender shoot (page 70)

¶ O CLAVIS DAVID

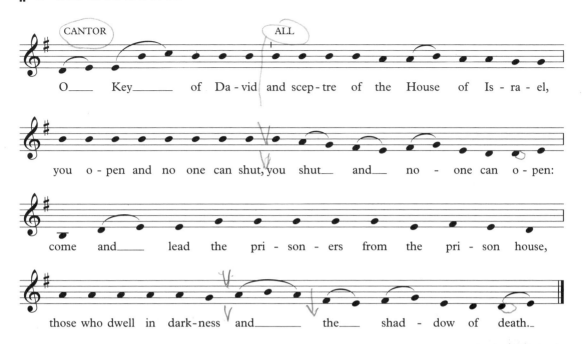

O___ Key___ of Da-vid and scep-tre of the House of Is-ra-el,

you o-pen and no one can shut, you shut__ and__ no - one can o-pen:

come and___ lead the pri - son - ers from the pri - son house,

those who dwell in dark-ness and___ the__ shad - dow of death._

Reading

The days are surely coming, says the Lord, when I will raise up for David a righteous Branch, and he shall reign as king and deal wisely, and shall execute justice and righteousness in the land. In his days Judah will be saved and Israel will live in safety. And this is the name by which he will be called: 'The Lord is our righteousness.'

Jeremiah 23: 5–6

Silence is kept

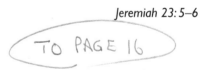
TO PAGE 16

Hymn

From the beginning, God's most holy word (page 14)
or
Like a candle flame (page 16)

or

Carol

David Ogden: O comfort my people (page 76)

Hymn: From the beginning, God's most holy word

GODMANCHESTER

Music: Peter Moger (b.1964)

1   From the beginning, God's most holy word
        Uttered the summons all creation heard;
        Christ, the word spoken, wisdom, pow'r and light,
        Transforms the darkness of the deepest night,

2   Summons to wholeness all God's love enfolds,
        Cherishes, nurtures, gently shapes, remoulds
        Structures that fail, the institution's blight,
        Bathes disappointment in transforming light.

3*   Jesus, the word once spoken by the well,
        Challenges, heals as in response we tell
        All our deep longings, all our hidden fears,
        Find then the solace of God's love and tears.

4*   Lord, we are here your blessed will to seek,
        May each one listen to the word you speak.
        Lord be our succour as we work and pray,
        Give us fresh purpose this and every day.

5*   Jesus, the word once spoken by the tomb,
        Speak to our hearts in times of doubt and gloom,
        Jesus the word, our life, our hope, our breath
        Draw us rejoicing from the sleep of death.

6   Jesus, you call each one of us to serve –
        Amazing grace we never could deserve.
        Here we renew our dedication's vow –
        Word of the Father, speak your summons now.

an arrangement of the last verse, with descant, can be found on page 75

Words © Brigid Pailthorpe
Music © Peter Moger
Used with permission

Alternative hymn
Hymn: Like a candle flame

Music: Graham Kendrick (b.1950)
arranged by David Ogden (b.1966)

♩ =92   **Simply, with a deep sense of stillness and expectation**

The Flute part is available to download from the RSCM website:
www.rscm.com/adventsequence

Come to save us, al - le - lu - ia.

al - le - lu - ia, al - le - lu - ia.

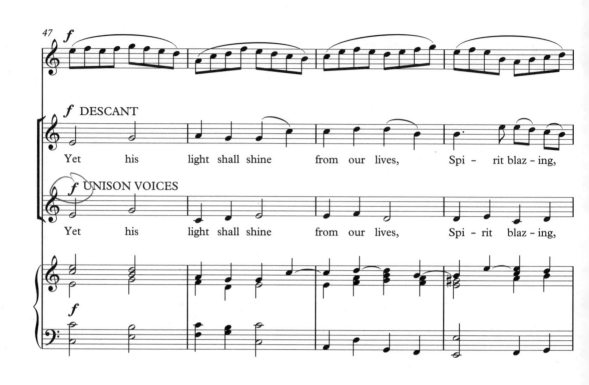

or

Carol

Irish trad. arr. David Ogden: O comfort my people (page 76)

TO PAGE 23

¶ O ORIENS

O_____ Mor - - ning Star,_____

splen-dour of light e - ter - nal____ and sun___ of___ righ-teous-ness:

Come and____ en - ligh - ten those who dwell in dark - ness

and the sha - - - dow___ of___ death.___

Reading

This is the testimony given by John when the Jews sent priests and Levites from Jerusalem to ask him, 'Who are you?' He confessed and did not deny it, but confessed, 'I am not the Messiah.' And they asked him, 'What then? Are you Elijah?' He said, 'I am not.' 'Are you the prophet?' He answered, 'No.' Then they said to him, 'Who are you? Let us have an answer for those who sent us. What do you say about yourself?' He said, 'I am the voice of one crying out in the wilderness, "Make straight the way of the Lord"', as the prophet Isaiah said.

Now they had been sent from the Pharisees. They asked him, 'Why then are you baptizing if you are neither the Messiah, nor Elijah, nor the prophet?' John answered them, 'I baptize with water. Among you stands one whom you do not know, the one who is coming after me; I am not worthy to untie the thong of his sandal.' This took place in Bethany across the Jordan where John was baptizing.

John 1: 19–28

Silence is kept

Canticle: Benedictus

Canticle: Blessed be the Lord the God of Israel (next page)
or
Anthem: Charles Villiers Stanford: Blessed be the Lord God of Israel (page 81)

Canticle: Blessed be the Lord the God of Israel

Noel Rawsthorne

1   Blessed be the Lord the ' God of ' Israel, ♦
     who has come to his ' people and ' set them ' free.

2   He has raised up for us a ' mighty ' Saviour, ♦
     born of the ' house of his ' servant ' David.

3   Through his holy prophets God ' promised of ' old ♦
     to save us from our enemies,from the ' hands of ' all that ' hate us,

4   To show mercy ' to our ' ancestors, ♦
     and to re'member his ' holy ' covenant.

5   This was the oath God swore to our ' father ' Abraham: ♦
     to set us ' free • from the ' hands of our ' enemies,

6   Free to worship him ' without ' fear, ♦
     holy and righteous in his sight' all the ' days of our ' life.

7   And you, child, shall be called the prophet of the ' Most ' High, ♦
     for you will go before the ' Lord • to pre'pare his ' way,

8   To give his people knowledge ' of sal'vation ♦
     by the for'giveness of ' all their ' sins.

9   In the tender compassion ' of our ' God ♦
     the dawn from on ' high shall ' break up'on us,

10   To shine on those who dwell in darkness and the ' shadow of ' death, ♦
     and to guide our feet ' into the ' way of ' peace.

Luke 1: 68–79

Glory to the Father and ' to the ' Son
and ' to the ' Holy ' Spirit;

as it was in the be'ginning is ' now
and shall be for ' ever. ' A'men.

from The Common Worship Psalter with Chants
words © The Archbishops' Council , 2000 and are used by permission
music © 2001, 2002 The Royal School of Church Music

¶ O REX GENTIUM

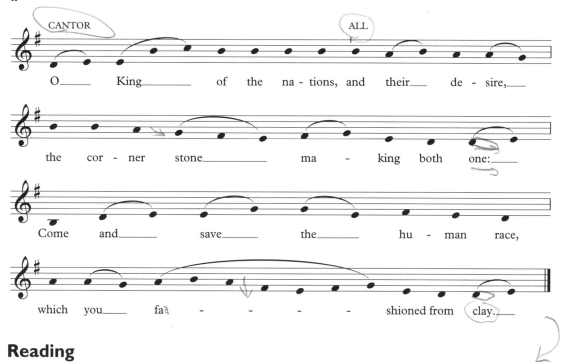

CANTOR

O King of the na-tions, and their de-sire,

ALL

the cor-ner stone ma-king both one:

Come and save the hu-man race,

which you faa - - - - shioned from clay.

Reading

I saw what appeared to be a sea of glass mixed with fire, and those who had conquered the beast and its image and the number of its name standing beside the sea of glass with harps of God in their hands. And they sing the song of Moses, the servant of God, and the song of the Lamb:

'Great and amazing are your deeds, Lord God the Almighty!
Just and true are your ways, King of the nations!
Lord, who will not fear and glorify your name?
For you alone are holy.
All nations will come and worship before you,
for your judgements have been revealed.'

Revelation 15: 2–4

Silence is kept

TO PAGE 28

Hymn

Come, thou long-expected Jesus (next page)
or
Christ, be our light (page 28)

Hymn: Come, thou long-expected Jesus

during which the light moves in procession to the East End

CROSS OF JESUS   Music: John Stainer (1840–1901)

1   Come, thou long-expected Jesus,
     Born to set thy people free,
     From our fears and sins release us,
     Let us find our rest in thee.

2   Israel's strength and consolation,
     Hope of all the earth thou art;
     Dear desire of every nation,
     Joy of every longing heart.

3   Born thy people to deliver,
     Born a child and yet a king,
     Born to reign in us for ever,
     Now thy gracious kingdom bring.

last verse descant opposite

4   By thine own eternal Spirit
     Rule in all our hearts alone;
     By thine all-sufficient merit
     Raise us to thy glorious throne.

Charles Wesley (1707–1788)

last verse arrangement and descant: Lindsay Gray (b.1953)

4. By thine own e – ter – nal_ Spi – rit rule in all our_ hearts a – lone;

by thine all – su – ffi – cient me – rit raise us to thy glor – ious throne.

alternative hymn

Hymn: Christ, be our light

during which the light moves in procession to the East End

UNISON

Words and Music: Bernadette Farrell (b.1957)

1. Long - ing for light,____ we wait in dark - ness.

Long - ing for truth,____ we turn to you.

Make us your own,____ your ho - ly peo - ple

light for the world to see.____

Refrain

DESCANT Last verse

Christ, be our light! Shine out through the dark shine!____

Christ, be our light! Shine in our hearts, shine through the dark - ness.

Christ____ be our light! Shine in your church

Christ, be our light! Shine in your Church

To verses   *Last time*

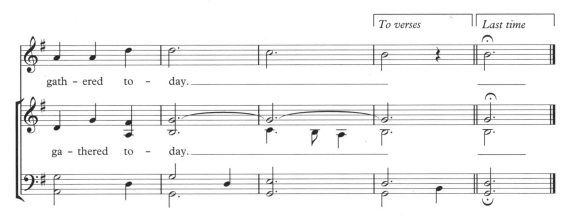

gath - ered to - day.____

ga - thered to - day.____

ALL 2   Longing for peace, our world is troubled.
u.   Longing for hope, many despair.
            Your word alone has power to save us.
            Make us your living voice. *Refrain*

LADIES 3   Longing for food, many are hungry.
            Longing for water, many still thirst.
            Make us your bread, broken for others,
            shared until all are fed.

MEN 4   Longing for shelter, many are homeless.
            Longing for warmth, many are cold.
            Make us your building, sheltering others,
            walls made of living stone.

ALL 5   Many the gifts, many the people,
u   many the hearts that yearn to belong.
            Let us be servants to one another,
            making your kingdom come.

TO PAGE 30

¶ O EMMANUEL

O——— Em - - - man - u - el,———

our king—————— and our—— law - gi - ver,

the hope—— of the na - tions and—— their—— Sa - viour:

Come and save—— us,—— O—— Lord our God.——

Reading

The birth of Jesus the Messiah took place in this way. When his mother Mary had been engaged to Joseph, but before they lived together, she was found to be with child from the Holy Spirit. Her husband Joseph, being a righteous man and unwilling to expose her to public disgrace, planned to dismiss her quietly.

But just when he had resolved to do this, an angel of the Lord appeared to him in a dream and said, 'Joseph, son of David, do not be afraid to take Mary as your wife, for the child conceived in her is from the Holy Spirit. She will bear a son, and you are to name him Jesus, for he will save his people from their sins.'

All this took place to fulfil what had been spoken by the Lord through the prophet: 'Look, the virgin shall conceive and bear a son, and they shall name him Emmanuel', which means, 'God is with us.'

Matthew 1: 18–23

Silence is kept

TO PAGE 102

Anthem

Richard Shephard: Wake, O wake! (page 95)
or
Mendelssohn: Sleepers, wake! (page 102)
or
George Guest: When came in flesh (page 107)

¶ THE CONCLUSION

Reading

I, John, heard a voice saying to me: 'See, I am coming soon; my reward is with me, to repay according to everyone's work. I am the Alpha and the Omega, the first and the last, the beginning and the end.

It is I, Jesus, who sent my angel to you with this testimony for the churches. I am the root and the descendant of David, the bright morning star.'
The Spirit and the bride say, 'Come.'
And let everyone who hears say, 'Come.'
And let everyone who is thirsty come.
Let anyone who wishes take the water of life as a gift.

The one who testifies to these things says, 'Surely I am coming soon.'
Amen. Come, Lord Jesus!

Revelation 22: 12–13, 16–17, 20

Hymn: Lo, he comes with clouds descending

during which the light returns in procession to the Chancel

HELMESLEY

Music: adapted by Thomas Olivers (1725–1798)
verse 4 arrangement by Martin How (b.1931)

1   Lo, he comes with clouds descending,
    once for favoured sinners slain;
    thousand thousand saints attending
    swell the triumph of his train:
    alleluia!
    God appears on earth to reign.

2   Every eye shall now behold him
    robed in dreadful majesty;
    those who set at naught and sold him,
    pierced and nailed him to the tree,
    deeply wailing,
    shall the true Messiah see.

3   Those dear tokens of his passion
    still his dazzling body bears;
    cause of endless exultation
    to his ransomed worshippers:
    with what rapture
    gaze we on those glorious scars.

for last verse arrangement, please turn over

4   Yea, amen, let all adore thee,
    high on thine eternal throne;
    Saviour, take the power and glory,
    claim the kingdom for thine own:
    alleluia!
    thou shalt reign, and thou alone.

Charles Wesley (1707–1788)
Martin Madan (1726–1790)
John Cennick (1718–1755)

4. Yea, A - men, let all_____ a - dore_____ thee,_____

4. Yea, A - men,_____ let_____ all_____ a - dore_____ thee,

high   on thine e - ter - nal_____ throne;_____

high   on thine e - ter - nal_____ throne;_____

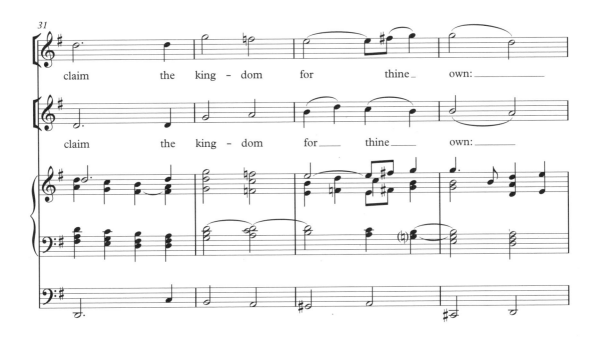

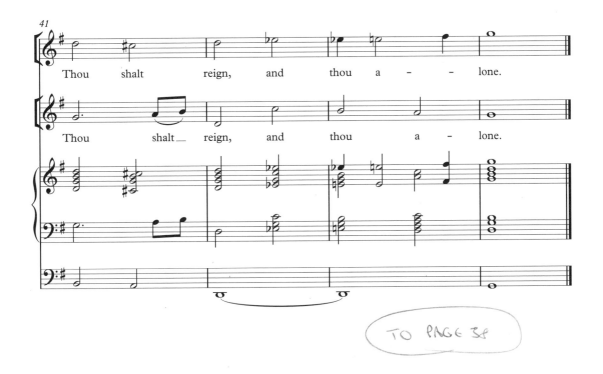

Thou shalt reign, and thou a - lone.

Thou shalt reign, and thou a - lone.

TO PAGE 38

PRAYERS

Let us pray.

Silence is kept

In joyful expectation of his coming to our aid
we pray to Jesus.

Come to your Church as Lord and Judge.
We pray for …
Help us to live in the light of your coming
and give us a longing for your Kingdom.
Maranatha:
Amen. Come, Lord Jesus.

Come to your world as King of the nations.
We pray for …
Before you rulers will stand in silence.
Maranatha:
Amen. Come, Lord Jesus.

Come to the suffering as Saviour and Comforter.
We pray for …
Break in to our lives
where we struggle with sickness and distress,
and set us free to serve you for ever.
Maranatha:
Amen. Come, Lord Jesus.

Come to us as shepherd and guardian of our souls.
We remember …
Give us with all the faithful departed
a share in your victory over evil and death.
Maranatha:
Amen. Come, Lord Jesus.

Come from heaven Lord Jesus with power and great glory.
Lift us up to meet you,
that with (*N* and) all your saints and angels
we may live and reign with you in your new creation.
Maranatha:

Amen. Come, Lord Jesus.

Common Worship: Times and Seasons

TO PAGE 42

Remain kneeling

Prayer response

Lord, you are the light of life to me (next page)
or
There is a longing in our hearts (page 42)

Hymn: Lord, you are the light of life to me (sung by the choir)

Words and music: Brian Hoare (b.1935)
arranged by David Iliff (b.1939)

alternative hymn
Hymn: There is a longing

Words and music: Anne Quigley

Let us pray for the coming of the Kingdom
in the words our Saviour gave us.

Our Father, who art in heaven,
Hallowed be thy Name,
Thy kingdom come,
Thy will be done, on earth as it is in heaven.
Give us this day our daily bread.
And forgive us our trespasses,
As we forgive those who trespass against us;
And lead us not into temptation,
But deliver us from evil.
For thine is the kingdom, the power and the glory,
For ever and ever. Amen.

Come, Lord Jesus, do not delay
give new courage to your people who trust in your love.
By your coming, raise us to share in the joy of your kingdom
on earth as in heaven,
where you live and reign
with the Father and the Spirit,
one God for ever and ever.
Amen.

Blessing

May God the Father,
who loved the world so much that he sent his only Son,
give you grace to prepare for life eternal.
Amen.

May God the Son,
who comes to us as Redeemer and Judge,
reveal to you the path from darkness to light.
Amen.

May God the Holy Spirit,
by whose working the Virgin Mary conceived the Christ,
help you bear the fruits of holiness.
Amen.

And the blessing of God almighty,
the Father, the Son, and the Holy Spirit,
be among you and remain with you always.
Amen.

Common Worship: Times and Seasons

Recessional Hymn: O come, O come, Emmanuel

during which the light moves in procession to the West End

VENI EMMANUEL

Music: from a French 13th-century missal
arranged by Noël Tredinnick (b.1949)
descant by David Iliff (b.1939)

1. O come, O come, Emmanuel, and
2. O come, true Branch of Jesse, free thine
3. O come, thou Day-spring, come and cheer our

ransom captive Israel, that
own from Satan's tyranny; from
spirits by thine advent here; dis-

mourns in lonely exile here un-
depths of hell thy people save, and
-perse the gloomy clouds of night, and

-til the Son of God appear:
give them victory o'er the grave:
death's dark shadows put to flight:

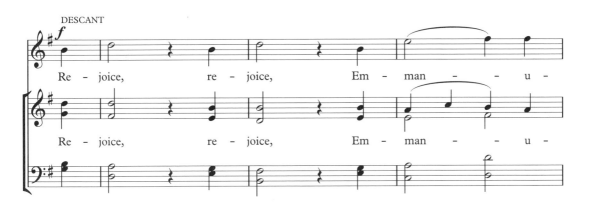

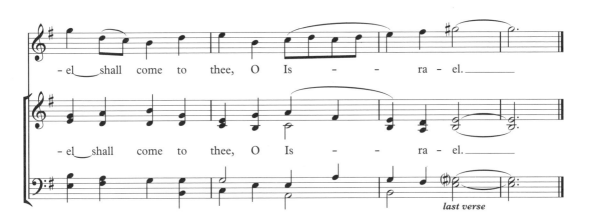

last verse

4. O come, thou Key of David, come,
and open wide our heavenly home;
make safe the way that leads on high,
and close the path to misery:
    Rejoice, rejoice, Emmanuel⌣
    shall come to thee, O Israel.

5. O come, O come thou Lord of Might,
who to thy tribes, on Sinai's height,
in ancient times didst give the law
in cloud and majesty and awe:
    Rejoice, rejoice, Emmanuel⌣
    shall come to thee, O Israel.

Words: from the Latin (13th century)
J M Neale (1818–1866) and others
Music arrangement © Noel Tredinnick / Jubilate Hymns,
Descant © David Iliff / Jubilate Hymns,
4 Thorne Park Road, Torquay TQ2 6RX
www.jubilate.co.uk USED BY PERMISSION

Dismissal

O Lord Jesus Christ, come at evening time with light,
and in the morning with your glory
to guide our feet into the way of peace.

He who receives our prayers says: Surely I come quickly.
I am the root and offspring of David, I am the bright and morning star.
Amen. Even so come, Lord Jesus.

Common Worship: Times and Seasons

a choral setting of the dismissal can be found on page 111

The congregation is asked to leave quietly

THE ADVENT SEQUENCE
PART II: CHORAL RESOURCES

The Blessing of the Light

Music: Peter Moger (b.1964)

CANTOR

Your word is a lan-tern to my feet:

and a light,____ and a light____ up-on our path.____

and a light,____ and a light up-on our path.____

and a light, and a light up - on our path.____

and a light,____ and a light up - on our path.____

The Advent Candle is lit

CANTOR

Je - sus Christ is the Light of the world.

A light____ no dark-ness_ can quench._____

A light____ no dark - ness,_ no dark-ness_ can quench.

A light____ no dark - ness,_ no dark-ness_ can quench.

A light____ no dark - ness,_ no dark-ness_ can quench.

go back to page 3

(Verses 2 + 4 Harmony)

This is the truth sent from above

Traditional Herefordshire Carol
collected and arranged by R Vaughan Williams (1872–1958)
this version by John Barnard (b.1948)

1. This is the truth sent from a-bove, the truth of God,_ the God of love, there - fore don't turn me_

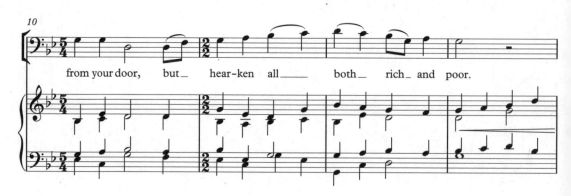

from your door, but_ hear-ken all_ both_ rich_ and poor.

2. The first thing which I do re-late, ___ is that God ___ did man cre-ate, ___ the

next thing which to ___ you I'll tell, wo - man was made ___ with ___ man to

dwell.   3. Then af-ter this ___ 'twas God's own choice to place them both in

SOPRANO and ALTO *mp*

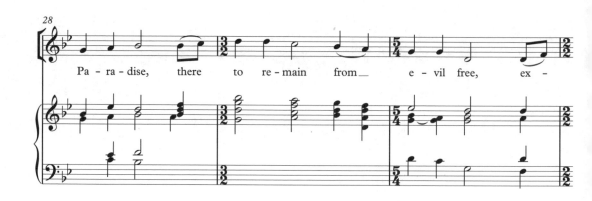

Pa - ra - dise, there to re - main from __ e - vil free, ex -

- cept they ate ____ of ____ such __ a tree.

4. And they did eat, ____ which was a sin, ____ and

thus their ru – in did be – gin;___ ru – ined them – selves, both___

you and me,   and___ all of their___ pos – te – ri – ty.

OPTIONAL DESCANT

5. Thus   we were heirs___ to end – less woes, till

ALL OTHER VOICES

5. Thus   we were heirs___ to end – less woes,   till

God the Lord did in - ter - pose, and so a pro - mise

God the Lord did in - ter - pose, and so a pro - mise

soon did run that he would re - deem us by his Son.

soon did run that he would re - deem us by his Son.

go back to page 7

Where shall wisdom be found?

Words: Job 28. 12, 28

Music: Peter Moger (b.1964)

Lord, that is wis-dom:_____

and to de-part from e - vil is un-der-

and to de-part from e - vil is un-der - stan-ding._____

-stan-ding._____

dim.

go back to page 7

Lord, all truth is from you

Words: from the Weekday Missal Week XXI

Music: Margaret Rizza (b.1929)

parts for descant soprano and various instruments are available to download from the website:
www.rscm.com/adventsequence

go back to page 7

Of a rose, a lovely rose

Words: Medieval anon.

Music: Jon Banks

SOPRANO SOLO *p*

Of a rose,   a love-ly rose,   of a rose is al myn song,   of a rose,   a love-ly rose,   of a rose is   al myn   song.

TENOR and BASS *mf*

List - neth

sheen; The rose is Ma — ry, hev-ne queen: Out of her bo-som the blos-mè

sprung.

Pray we to her with_ great ho - nour, She_ that bare the bles-sèd

flower: She be our help and our suc - cour, And shield us from the_ fien-dès

go back to page 13

For Gwen

A Tender Shoot

Words: William Bartholomew (1793–1867)

Music: Simon Lole (b.1957)

A ten - der shoot has___ start - ed

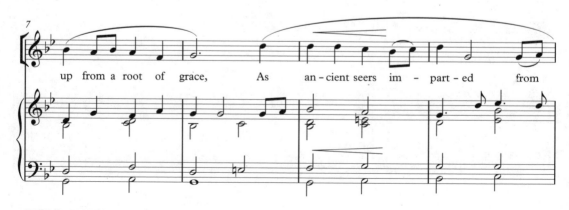

up from a root of grace, As an - cient seers im - part - ed from

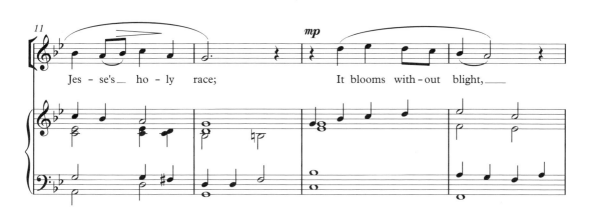

Jes - se's— ho - ly race; It blooms with - out blight,—

it blooms with - out blight,— Blooms in the cold bleak

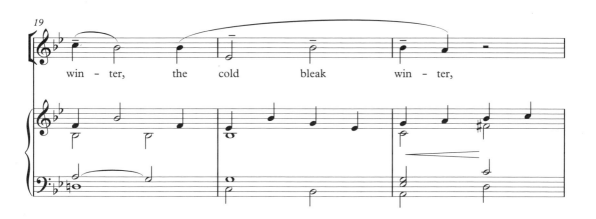

win - ter, the cold bleak win - ter,

go back to page 13

Hymn Tune: 'Godmanchester' last verse

Music: Peter Moger (b.1964)

go back to page 23

O Comfort my people

Words: Chrysogonus Waddell (1930–2008)
based on Isaiah 40

Traditional Irish
arranged by David Ogden (b.1966)

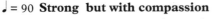

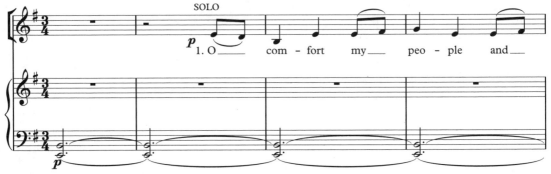

go back to page 23

Benedictus

Words: Luke 1: 68–79

Music: Charles Villiers Stanford (1852–1924)
Op.115

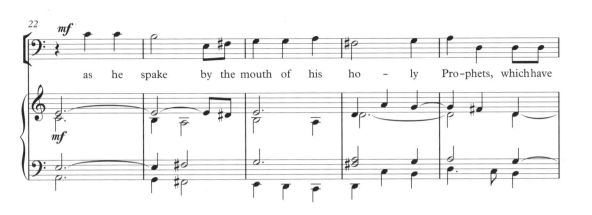

as he spake by the mouth of his ho — ly Pro-phets, which have

That we should be sa-ved from our

been since the world be - gan; That we should be sa-ved from our

en - e-mies, and from the hands of all that hate us,

en - e-mies, and from the hands of all that hate us,

to per-form the oath which he sware to our fore-fa - ther A - bra-

to per-form the oath which he sware to our fore-fa - ther A - bra-

to per-form the oath which he sware to our fore-fa - ther A - bra-

to per-form the oath which he sware to our fore-fa - ther A - bra-

Moderato con moto ♩ = 100

-ham, that he would give us, that we be - ing de - liv-er-ed out of the

-ham, that he would give us, that we be - ing de - liv-er-ed out of the

-ham, that he would give us, that we be - ing de - liv-er-ed out of the

-ham, that he would give us, that we be - ing de - liv-er-ed out of the

Moderato con moto ♩ = 100

life. And thou, child, shalt be call-ed the Pro — phet of the High - est:

life.

life.

life.

for thou shalt go_____ be - fore the face of the Lord   to pre-pare   his

ways; _____ To give know-ledge of sal-

To pre-pare his _____ ways;

To pre-pare his ways;

To pre-pare his ways;

-va - tion un - to his peo - ple

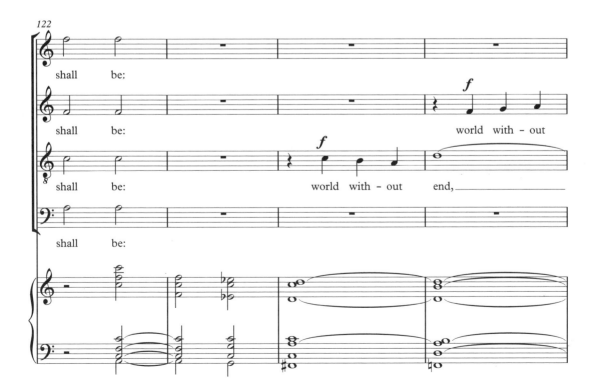

go back to page 25

Wake, O wake!

Words: Philipp Nicolai (1556–1608)
translated C Burkitt (1864–1935)

Music: Richard Shephard (b.1949)

1. Mid-night strikes! no more de-lay - ing,   'The hour has come!' we hear them say - ing,   Where are ye all, ye vir-gins wise?   Bride-groom comes in sight,___ Raise high your tor - ches
2. See her Friend from heav'n de-scend - ing,   A-dorned with truth and grace un-end - ing!   Her light burns clear, her star doth rise.   come, thou pre - cious crown,___ Lord Je - su, God's own

The
Now

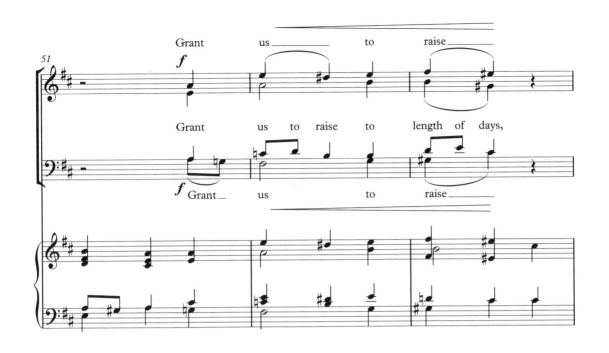

go back to page 31

Sleepers, wake!

Music: F Mendelssohn (1809–1847)

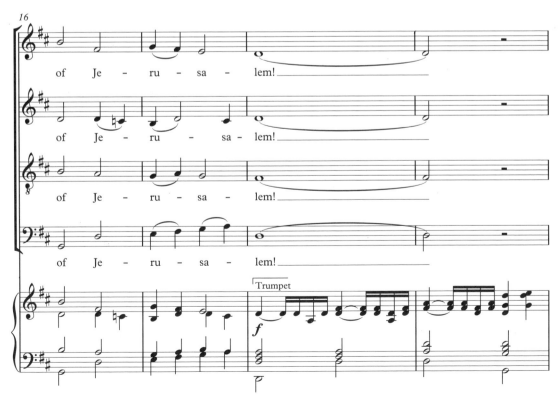

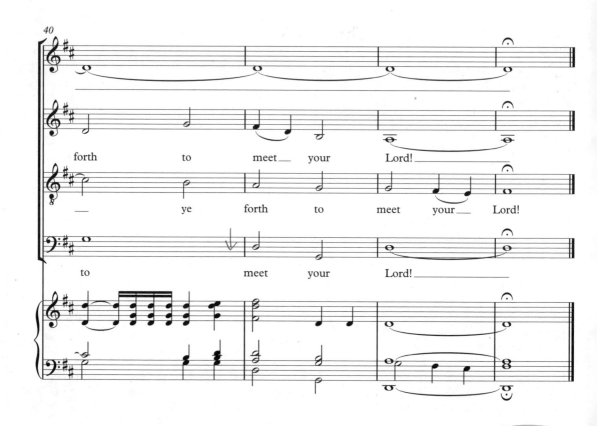

go back to page 31

When came in flesh

Words: J Anstice (1805–1836)

Music: from *A Choice Collection of Psalm Tunes*
W Anchors c.1721
arranged by George Guest (1924–2002)

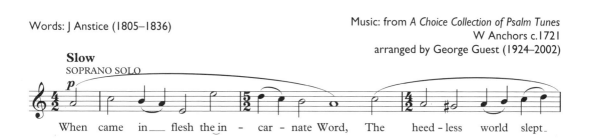

When came in flesh the in-car-nate Word, The heed-less world slept

on, And on-ly sim-ple shep-herds heard That

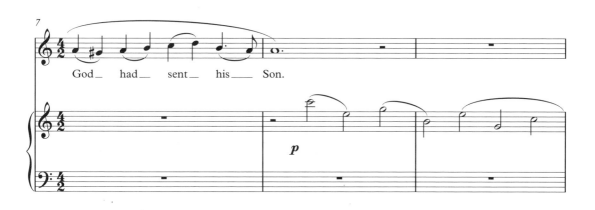

God had sent his Son.

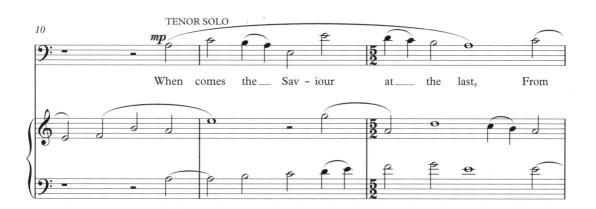

When comes the Sav-iour at the last, From

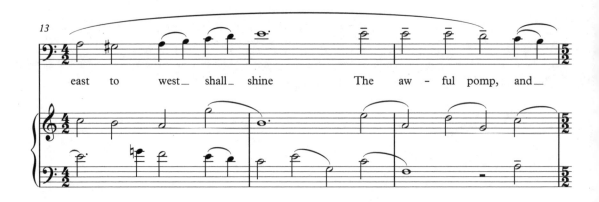

east to west__ shall__ shine   The   aw - ful pomp, and__

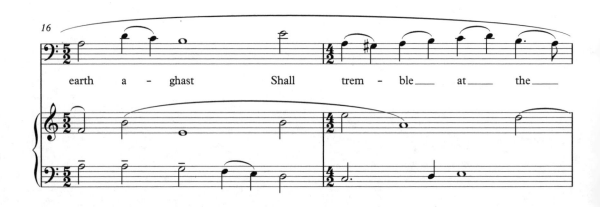

earth   a - ghast   Shall   trem - ble__ at__ the__

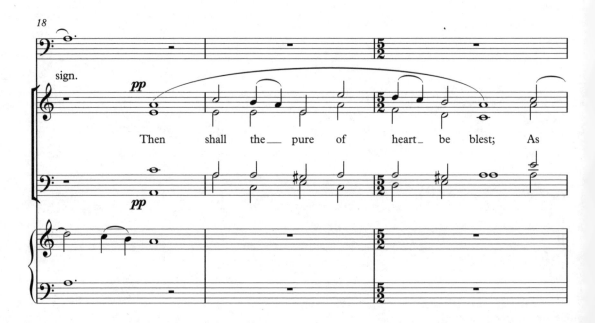

sign.   *pp*   Then   shall   the__ pure   of   heart__ be   blest;   As

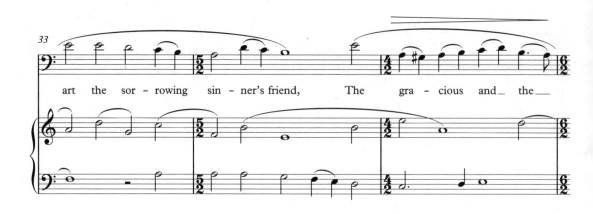

art the sor - rowing sin - ner's friend, The gra - cious and _ the _

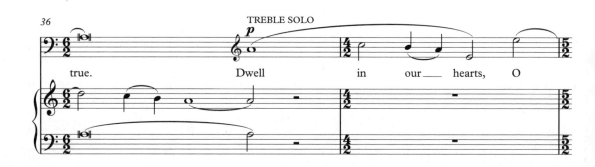

TREBLE SOLO

true.   Dwell   in   our _ hearts,   O

Sav - iour blest,   So   shall   thine   Ad - vent's _

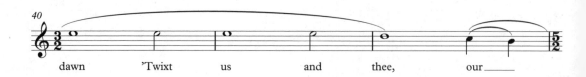

dawn   'Twixt   us   and   thee,   our _

poco rit.

bo - som _ guest,   Be   but _ the _ veil _ with - drawn.

go back to page 31

Advent closing responses

Music: Peter Moger (b.1964)

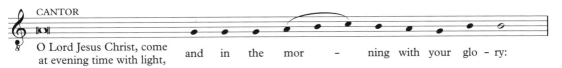

CANTOR

O Lord Jesus Christ, come / at evening time with light, and in the mor - ning with your glo - ry:

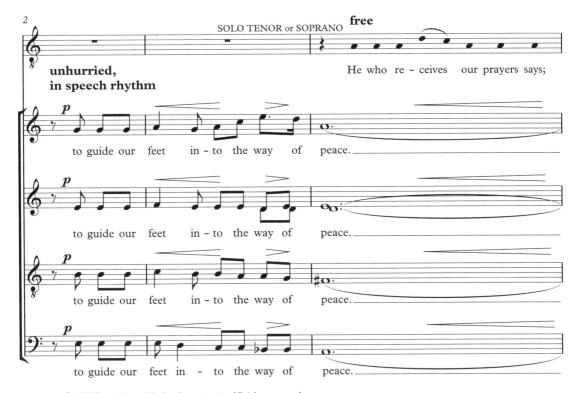

2

SOLO TENOR or SOPRANO   **free**

He who re - ceives   our prayers says;

**unhurried,
in speech rhythm**

p
to guide our   feet   in - to   the way   of   peace._____

p
to guide our   feet   in - to   the way   of   peace._____

p
to guide our   feet   in - to   the way   of   peace._____

p
to guide our   feet in - to   the way   of   peace._____

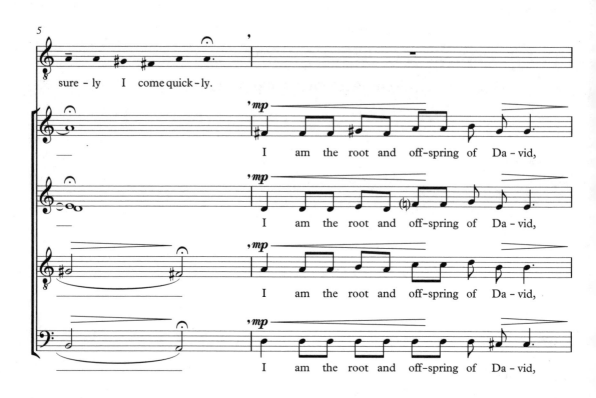

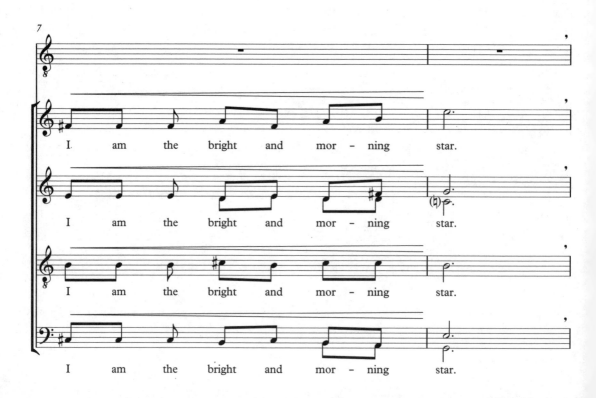

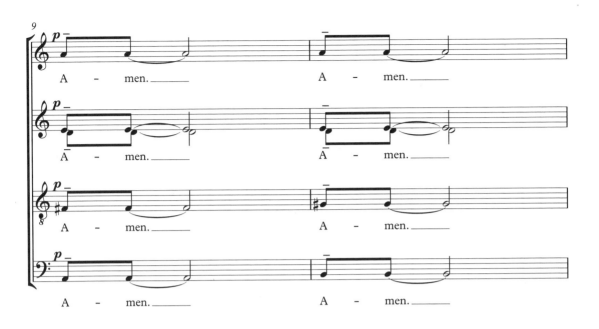

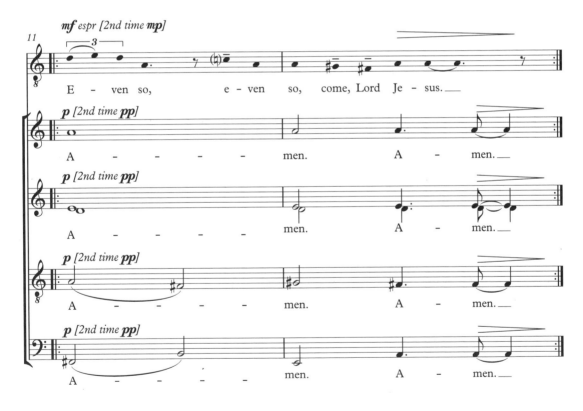

THE GREAT ADVENT 'O'S

O Sapientia

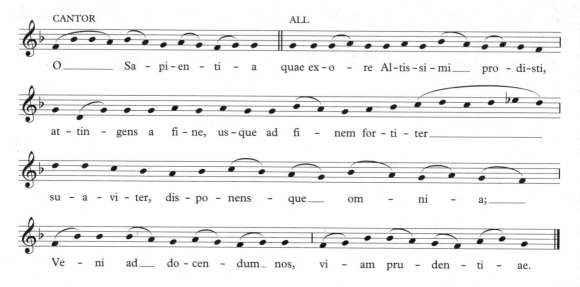

CANTOR

ALL

O_____ Sa - pi - en - ti - a   quae ex - o - re Al - tis - si - mi___ pro - di - sti,

at - tin - gens a fi - ne, us - que ad fi - nem for - ti - ter_____

su - a - vi - ter, dis - po - nens - que__ om - ni - a;_____

Ve - ni ad__ do - cen - dum_ nos, vi - am pru - den - ti - ae.

O Adonaï

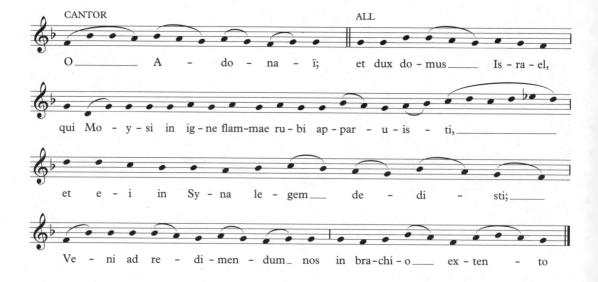

CANTOR

ALL

O_____ A - do - na - ï;   et dux do - mus___ Is - ra - el,

qui Mo - y - si in ig - ne flam - mae ru - bi ap - par - u - is - ti,_____

et e - i in Sy - na le - gem_ de - di - sti;_____

Ve - ni ad re - di - men - dum_ nos in bra - chi - o___ ex - ten - to

O Radix Jesse

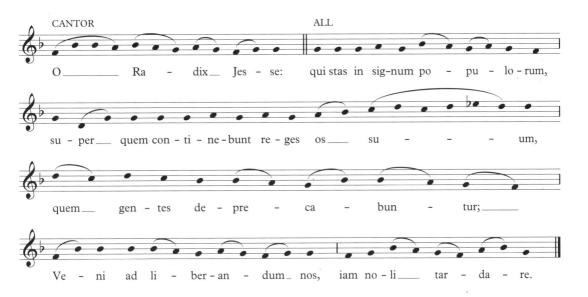

O Clavis David

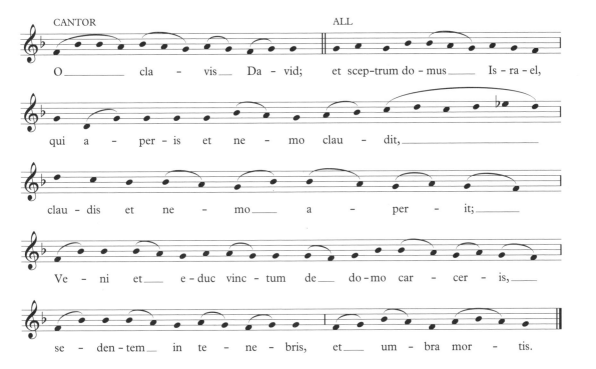

O Oriens

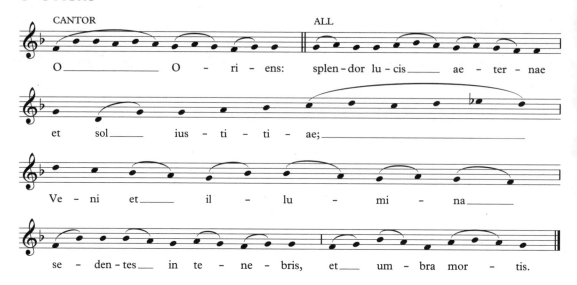

O Rex Gentium

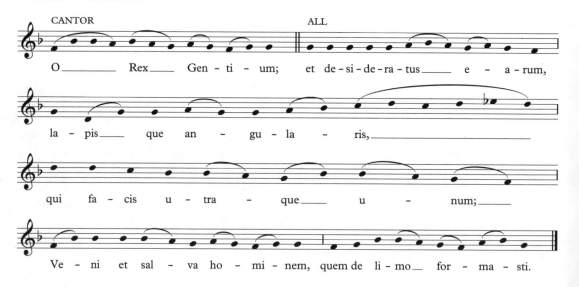

O Emmanuel

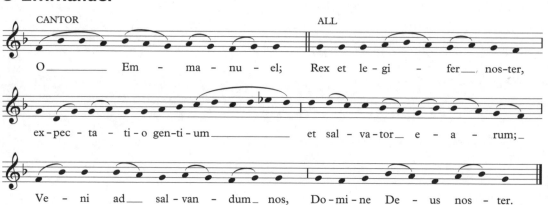